PLANTS

Written by Linda Schwartz
Illustrated by Beverly Armstrong

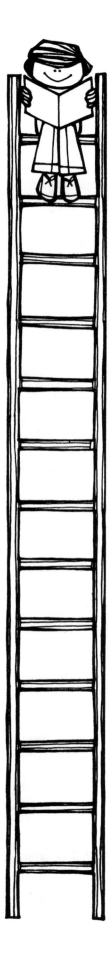

The Learning Works

Edited by Sherri M. Butterfield

The purchase of this book entitles the individual classroom teacher to reproduce copies for use in the classroom.

The reproduction of any part for an entire school or school system or for commercial use is strictly prohibited.

Copyright © 1990
The Learning Works, Inc.
Santa Barbara, California 93160
All rights reserved.
Printed in the United States of America.

Write for information about our educational products.
The Learning Works • Box 6187, Dept. N • Santa Barbara, CA 93160

To the Teacher

PLANTS is a Learning Works mini-unit especially created for children in grades one through four. The purpose of this unit is to blend the presentation of facts about plants with the practice of primary skills to produce the very best in theme-related teaching and results-oriented learning.

Information about plants is presented in a question-and-answer format. From easy-to-read passages, kids learn what plants are, how they differ from other living things, why plants are important to us, what parts most plants have, how green plants make food, and how plants grow. Associated activities involve primary-aged children in observing and comparing, classifying, identifying and labeling, ordering and sequencing, locating and using information, and following directions. These tasks are carefully designed to improve hand-eye coordination; increase skill in visual discrimination, word recognition, phonics, and spelling; stimulate curiosity; and foster creative expression.

In addition to information and activity sheets, this book also includes a page of fascinating plant facts, a two-page glossary of plant terms, and a **Budding Botanist Award**.

Although this book was created for students, the teacher has not been forgotten. For your convenience, we have included two **All-Purpose Worksheets**, one featuring leaves and the other filled with fruit. You can reproduce either one of these sheets, add content—plant words to be looked up, spelling words to be learned, math problems to be worked—and reproduce again so that you will have one for every member of your class.

This book also contains instructions for six **Correlated Activities** suitable for small-group or whole-class projects, **Special Plant Awards** with which you can thank classroom helpers and recognize outstanding effort, and **Plant Clip Art** you can use to decorate announcements, bulletins, fliers, game boards, invitations, name tags, newsletters, notes, and programs.

This mini-unit offers stimulating activities in a botanical context so that primary learners can strengthen their skill in essential areas while increasing their knowledge about plants.

Contents

Name _____

What Is a Plant?

A **plant** is any living thing that is *not* an animal. Like animals, plants grow to be many different sizes. Some plants are very large, and some are very small. Unlike animals, plants cannot think or move from place to place by themselves. Trees, shrubs, grasses, and herbs are plants. Kelp and cactus are plants. Even the algae that grow in aquariums and swimming pools are plants. The oldest and tallest living things on earth are plants. Color the plants in this picture.

Why Are Plants Important to Us?

We could not live without plants. The oxygen in the air we breathe comes from plants. Plants give us many of the foods we eat. Cereals, flours, fruits, vegetables, and spices all come from plants. Paper, rubber, wood, and many medicines are made from plants. We get cotton and linen for our clothes from plants. Plants also give us shade and make our world more beautiful.

All of the foods in this picture come from plants. Color the picture.

On a separate sheet of paper, draw a picture of three things in your classroom that come from plants.

Name _____

What Are the Parts of a Plant?

The four most important parts of a plant are the roots, the stem, the leaves, and the flowers. The **roots** take water and minerals from the earth. The **stem** acts as a pipeline to carry the water and minerals to the leaves. The **leaves** use the water and minerals to make food for the plant so it will grow and bloom. The **flowers** make seeds so that there will be more plants. Name the parts of this plant by writing the word **root,**   **stem,**   **leaf,**   or   **flower** in each box. Then color the picture.

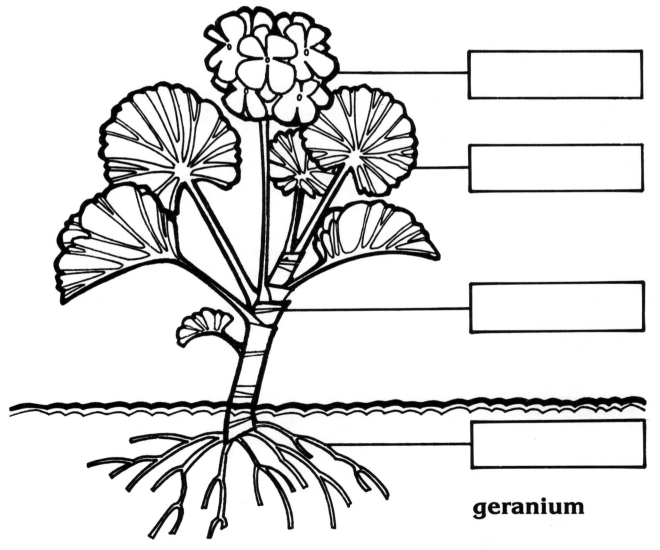

geranium

What Do the Roots Do?

The **roots** of a plant grow down into the earth. They soak up water and minerals to feed the plant. They also hold the plant in place so it will not fall down or blow away.

The roots of all plants are not alike. The roots of some plants are thick and strong. The roots of other plants are thin and easily broken. The roots of some plants lie near the surface. The roots of other plants reach very deep. The roots of some plants stay close together. The roots of other plants spread far apart. We can safely eat the roots of some plants. The roots of other plants will make us sick.

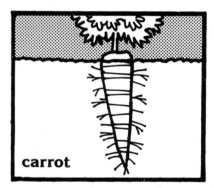
carrot

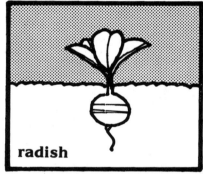
radish

pine tree

We eat the roots of beet, carrot, and radish plants.

yucca

The roots of many desert plants are close together and lie near the surface so they can catch a lot of water when it rains.

The pine tree sends a taproot deep into the earth.

Name _____

Root Maze

Plant roots find their way into cracks, grow around rocks, and even lift pieces of cement driveways, patios, and sidewalks. Help the roots of this plant find their way to the water. With your pencil, mark a path for them to follow through the maze.

plant roots

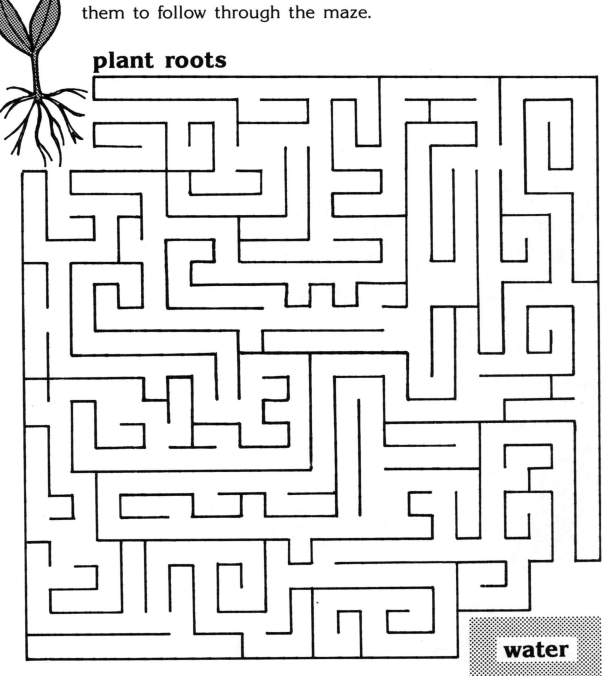

water

What Does the Stem Do?

The **stem** of a plant holds up the leaves and flowers. It also carries water and minerals from the roots to other parts of the plant.

The stems of all plants are not alike. The stems of some plants are stiff and woody. These stems are called **trunks**. The stems of other plants are soft and bendable. These stems are called **stalks**. We eat the stalks of asparagus, broccoli, celery, and rhubarb plants. In the plant pictures below, color the stems.

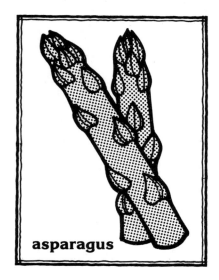

asparagus

broccoli

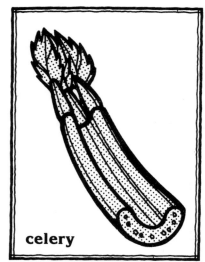

celery

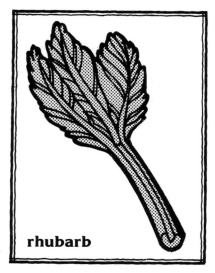

rhubarb

aspen

Name _____

What Do the Leaves Do?

The **leaves** are the green parts of a plant. They make food for the plant. They also help the plant breathe.

Leaves are usually flat and thin. But not all leaves are the same shape. The leaves of pine trees are called **needles**. They are long, thin, and pointed.

Some leaves are **round**.

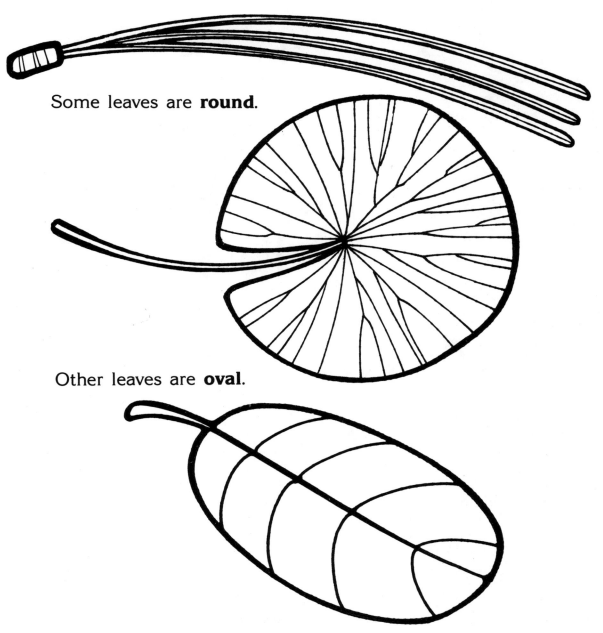

Other leaves are **oval**.

Name _____

What Do the Leaves Do?
(continued)

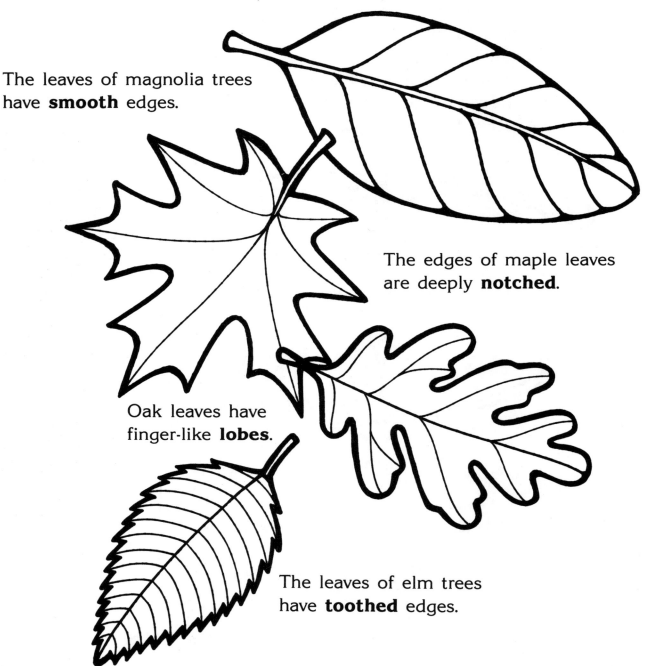

The leaves of magnolia trees have **smooth** edges.

The edges of maple leaves are deeply **notched**.

Oak leaves have finger-like **lobes**.

The leaves of elm trees have **toothed** edges.

Color the leaves on pages 11 and 12. The next time you look at a plant, notice the shape of its leaves. See how many different leaf shapes you can find.

Name _____

Which Leaf Is Different?

In each row of leaves, one leaf is different. Find
and color the different leaf.

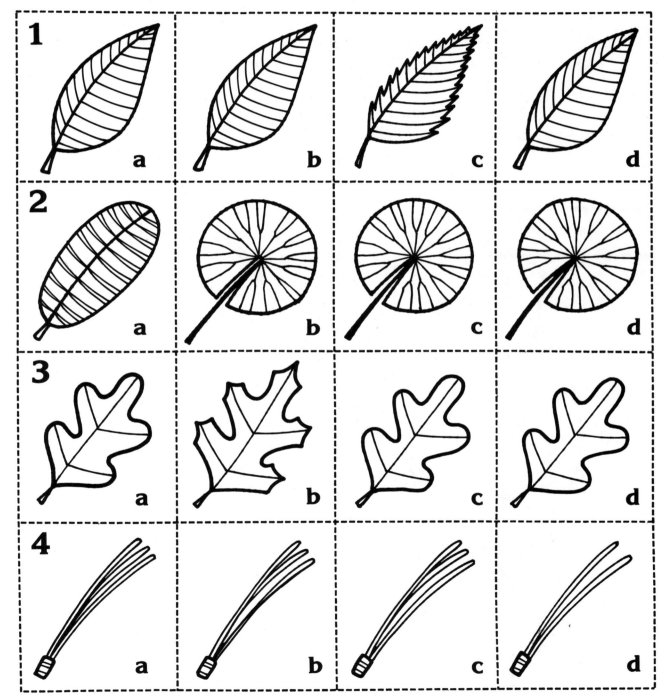

Name _____

What Are the Parts of a Leaf?

The four most important parts of a leaf are the blade, the stem, the midrib, and the veins. The **blade** is the broad flat body of the leaf. The **stem** connects the blade to the plant. The **midrib** is the central vein of the leaf. It runs from the base of the blade to its tip. The **veins** carry water from the midrib to all parts of the blade. Name the parts of this leaf by writing the word

blade,   **stem,**   **midrib,**   or   **veins**

in each box. Then color the picture.

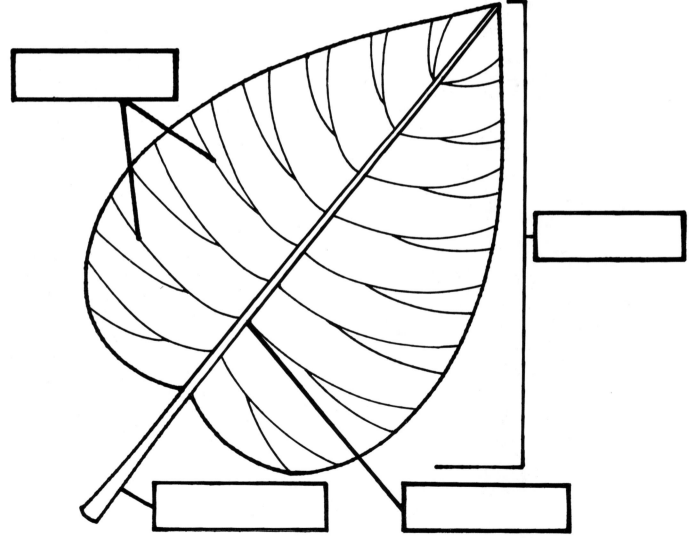

How Do Leaves Make Food?

The leaves of green plants contain **chlorophyll** (KLOR' - uh - fill). This green material gives the leaves their color. It also enables them to make their own food.

The top and bottom of each leaf are covered with tiny holes. Air comes into the leaf through these holes. Water enters the leaf through the stem. Using light for energy, chlorophyll combines the air and water to make sugars and starches.

These sugars and starches are stored in the leaves and stems of the plant. The plant uses them for food. People use them for food, too.

We eat the leaves of cabbage, lettuce, and spinach plants.

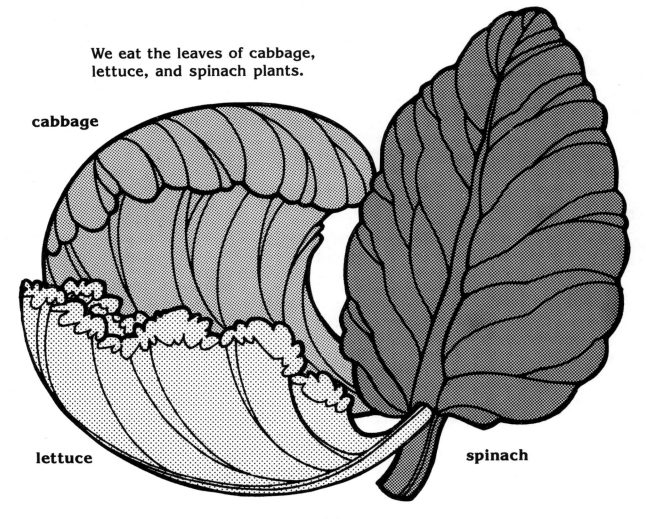

cabbage

lettuce

spinach

Name _____

Chlorophyll Crossword

Use the numbered clues to write the correct words in the squares. The nine words you will need are listed in the box below.

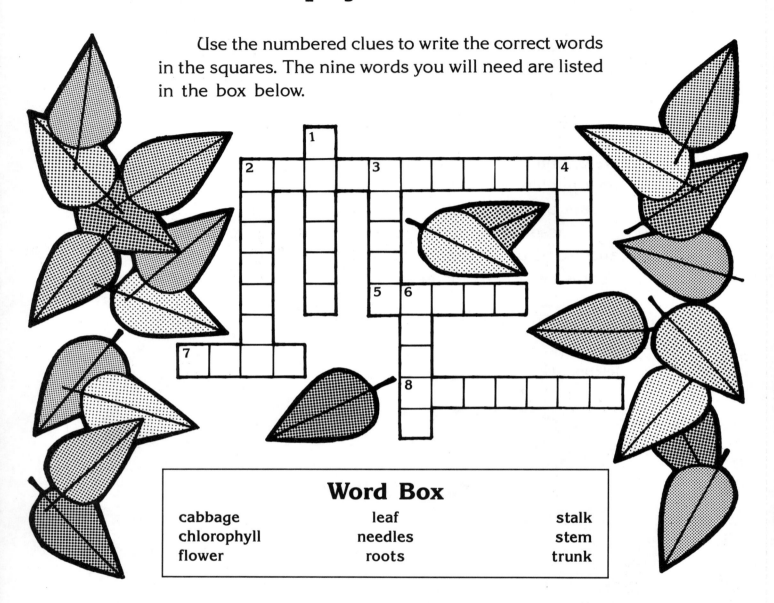

Word Box

cabbage	leaf	stalk
chlorophyll	needles	stem
flower	roots	trunk

Across

2. The green stuff that gives leaves their color and enables them to make food.
5. The soft bendable stem of a plant like asparagus or celery.
7. The part of a plant that holds up the leaves and flowers.
8. Another name for pine tree leaves.

Down

1. The part of a plant that blooms and makes seeds.
2. A plant whose leaves are good to eat.
3. The part of a plant that takes water and minerals from the earth.
4. The part of a plant that makes food and helps the plant breathe.
6. The stem of a tree.

What Do Flowers Do?

Flowers come in many sizes, shapes, and colors. They look pretty. Some of them smell good. Flowers make seeds so there will be more plants. Color this picture of flowers.

Name _____

What Are the Parts of a Flower?

The four most important parts of a flower are the
sepals, the petals, the pistil, and the stamens.

The **sepals** are special leaves that
cover and protect the flower bud while
it is growing. When the flower is ready
to bloom, the sepals open and peel back
to let the petals out.

The **petals** are the most noticeable
part of the flower. They are often bright
colors. The petals make insects see the
flower and come to it.

The **pistil** is usually found in the
very center of the flower. It is sticky and
is the part of the flower that makes seeds.

The **stamens** are grouped around
the pistil. They are taller than the pistil
and are often yellow. They hold pollen.
Pollen is a powderlike dust that helps
the flower make seeds.

Color this picture of a rose.

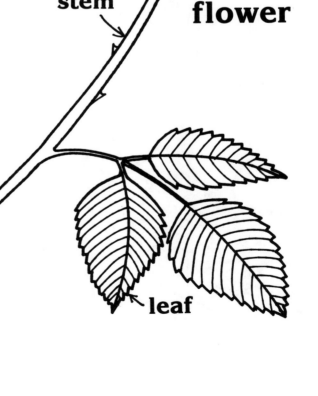

petals

stamens

pistil

seeds

sepals

stem

flower

bud

sepals

thorn →

leaf

Name _____

Flower Power

Write the names of these flowers in ABC order on the lines below.

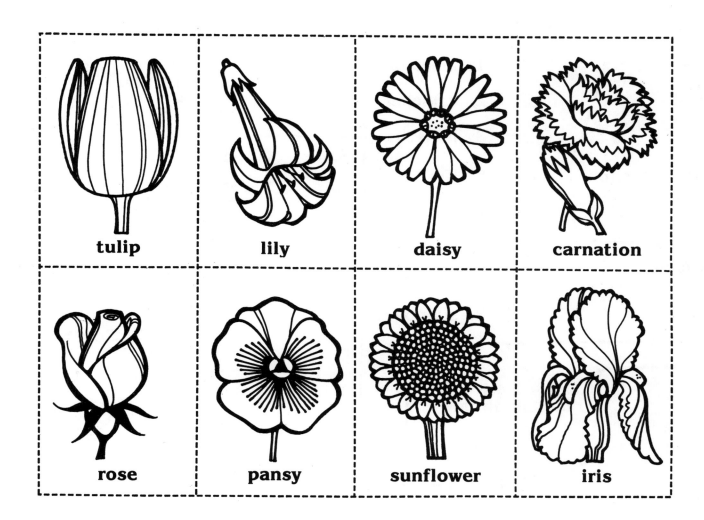

1. _____   5. _____

2. _____   6. _____

3. _____   7. _____

4. _____   8. _____

Name _____

State Flower Match-Up

Each state in the United States of America has a special flower. First, use books to learn about these flowers. Then, match the eight flowers listed below with their states by writing a letter on each line.

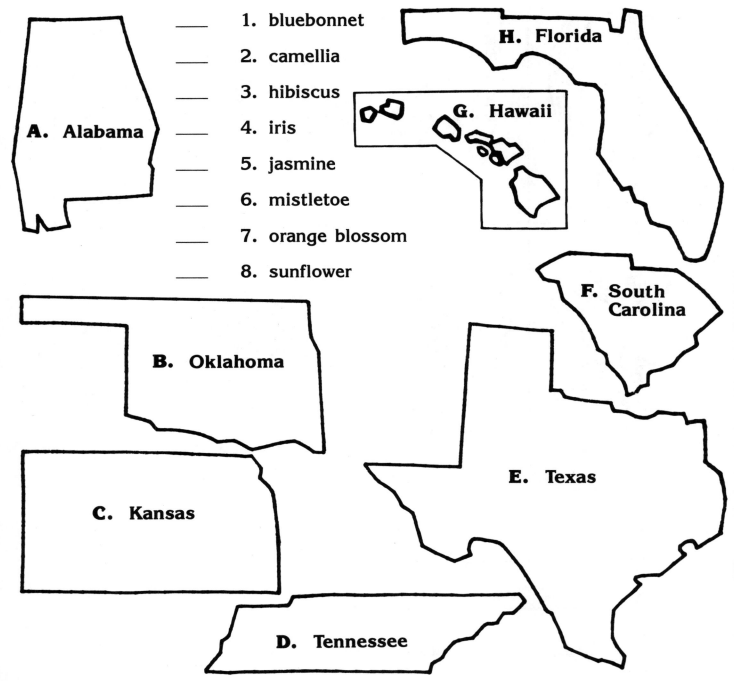

____ 1. bluebonnet

____ 2. camellia

____ 3. hibiscus

____ 4. iris

____ 5. jasmine

____ 6. mistletoe

____ 7. orange blossom

____ 8. sunflower

H. Florida

G. Hawaii

A. Alabama

F. South Carolina

B. Oklahoma

E. Texas

C. Kansas

D. Tennessee

Name _____

Design a Stamp

Design a stamp in honor of a plant. The plant can be a tree, shrub, herb, grass, or cactus. The stamp should include a picture of the plant, the name of the plant, the name of the country issuing the stamp, and the amount of money the stamp will sell for.

What Is a Seed?

A **seed** is a baby plant wrapped in a very special package. This package has a hard shell that protects the tiny plant. This package holds food for the new plant to use until it grows leaves and can make its own food.

There is a small hole in the shell. This hole lets water go inside the seed. If a seed is kept dry, the baby plant will not grow. Once water gets inside the seed, the baby plant gets bigger and pushes its way out of the shell. The seed sprouts.

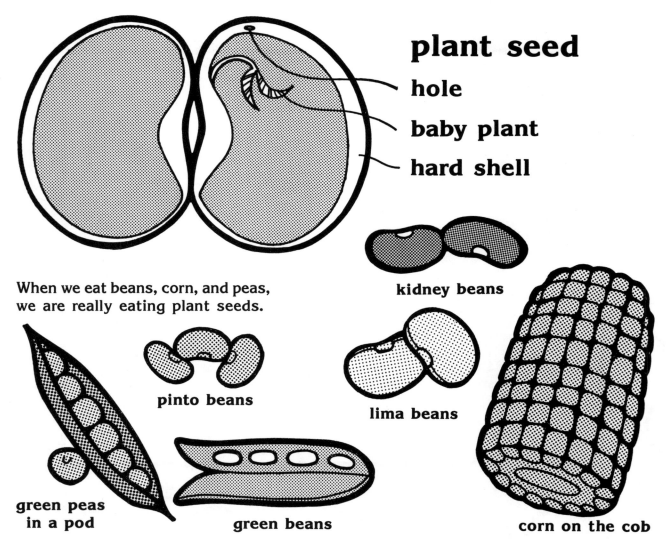

plant seed

hole

baby plant

hard shell

kidney beans

When we eat beans, corn, and peas, we are really eating plant seeds.

pinto beans

lima beans

green peas in a pod

green beans

corn on the cob

Name _____

Try This!

1. On Monday, get a tray or a cookie sheet with a rim.

2. Run water on eight paper towels.

3. Squeeze out the towels so they are *not* dripping wet.

4. Lay four damp towels on the tray. Stack the towels, in pairs, one atop the other.

5. Scatter alfalfa or bean seeds on the damp towels.

6. Lay the other four damp towels on top of the seeds.

7. Place the tray where the towels will *not* be dried out by direct sunlight or a draft.

8. Each day, sprinkle water on the towels to keep them damp.

9. On Friday, carefully lift the top towels to see what has happened to the seeds. Have they sprouted?

10. If the seeds have not sprouted, cover them, keep them damp for another week, and then look again.

Sprouted seeds should look like this.

Name _____

A Seed Becomes a Plant

Cut out the pictures. Paste them on the squares to show the order in which things happen when a seed becomes a plant.

1	2	3
4	5	6

Name _____

What Does a Seed Need to Grow?

A seed needs water to sprout, but it must have other things to grow into a plant. It must have water. It must have warmth. And it must have air.

A Plant Grows

How does a plant grow? Number these steps to show the order in which things happen when a plant grows. Put a **1** in front of the thing that happens first. Put a **2** in front of the thing that happens next, and so on.

_____   The swollen plant bursts out of the seed.

_____   The water soaks into the seed.

_____   A seed is placed in the ground and watered.

_____   A tiny root pushes down into the soil.

_____   The water makes the plant and food inside the seed swell up.

_____   A stem with leaves springs out of the ground, reaching for the sunshine.

What Is a Fruit?

A **fruit** is the part of a plant that holds the seeds. Many kinds of fruits are good to eat. Some fruits— such as apples, avocados, cherries, oranges, peaches, pears, and plums—grow on trees. Strawberries, rasp- berries, and blueberries grow on bushes. Cranberries, grapes, tomatoes, and watermelons grow on vines. Color these fruits.

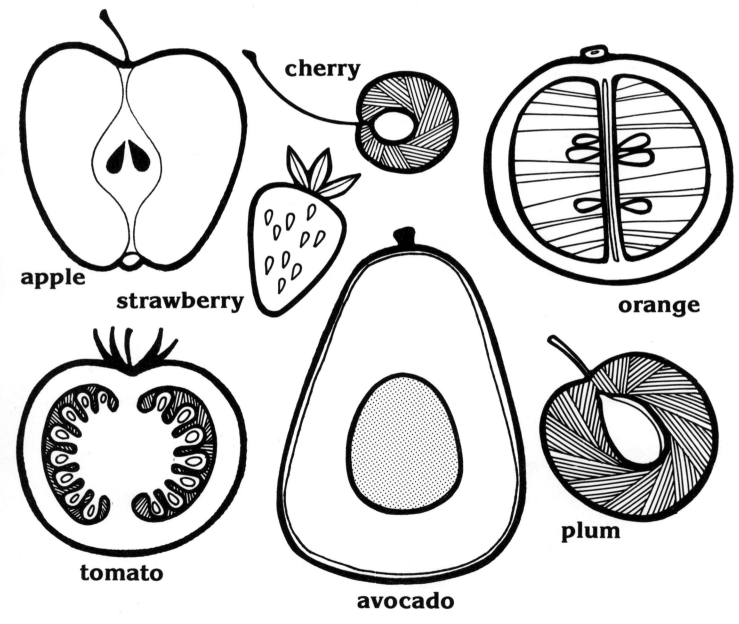

apple

cherry

strawberry

orange

tomato

avocado

plum

Name _____

Which Picture Is Different?

In each row, one picture is different. Find and color the different picture.

1			
a	b	c	d

2			
a	b	c	d

3			
a	b	c	d

4			
a	b	c	d

Name _____

A Nutty Puzzle

The ten nuts listed in the word box are the seeds of trees. The names of these nuts have been hidden in this puzzle. Find and circle them.

```
B  U  T  T  E  R  N  U  T  M
C  L  H  I  C  K  O  R  Y  A
A  V  W  X  O  Z  A  H  A  C
S  F  P  E  C  A  N  A  L  A
H  P  Q  R  O  T  U  Z  M  D
E  Z  A  B  N  D  E  E  O  A
W  J  K  L  U  N  O  L  N  M
R  T  U  V  T  X  Y  N  D  I
C  D  E  W  A  L  N  U  T  A
C  H  E  S  T  N  U  T  K  Y
```

Word Box

almond • butternut • cashew • chestnut • coconut
hazelnut • hickory • macadamia • pecan • walnut

Name _____

Strawberry Spelling

More than one hundred words can be made from the letters in the word

strawberry.

How many of these words can you find? Follow the game rules. Write your words on the lines below. If you need more space, use the back of this page or a separate sheet of paper.

Game Rules

1. Each word you write must have three or more letters.
2. You may list and count plurals.
3. You may use the letters in any order.
4. In any one word, you may use a letter only as often as it appears in the word **strawberry.**

Examples: You may write **try**, but you may not write **sassy**.
You may write **bats**, but you may not write **straws**.

What Are Grasses?

Grasses are one large group of green plants. Most grasses have jointed stems and long narrow leaves called **blades**. When grasses bloom, they produce spikelike clusters of flowers. Grasses grow easily on flat open land. They cover fields, pastures, and yards.

There are many different kinds of grasses. Bermuda, Kentucky bluegrass, and rye are lawn grasses. Barley, corn, oats, rice, and wheat are grasses, too. These grasses are called **cereals**. They are grown by farmers. Their seeds are called **grain**. Grain is one of the most important foods we get from plants. Our breakfast cereals, the flour we use to make breads and cookies, and the kernels we heat to make popcorn all come from grasses.

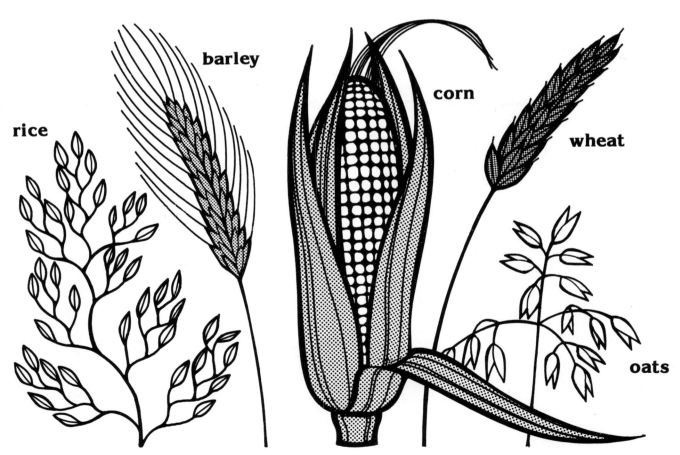

rice

barley

corn

wheat

oats

Name _____

Graph a Grain

Take a vote to find out which breakfast cereal your classmates like best. First, ask the boys and girls in your class to name the cereals they eat most often. Write the cereals they name on the lines below.

1. _____ ☐   4. _____ ☐

2. _____ ☐   5. _____ ☐

3. _____ ☐   6. _____ ☐

Next, read these names aloud, one at a time. Ask the boys and girls to hold up their hands when they hear the names of their favorite cereals. Tell them to vote only once. Each time you read the name of a cereal, count the number of hands. Write that number in the box beside the cereal name.

Finally, in the space below, draw a bar graph to show the results of this vote. Write the names of the cereals on the numbered lines. Draw a line in each row to show the number of votes that cereal got. Color each row all the way across from the line labeled 0 to the line you drew.

Names of Cereals						
1.						
2.						
3.						
4.						
5.						
6.						

0   5   10   15   20   25   30

Number of Votes

Do All New Plants Come from Seeds?

No, all new plants do not come from seeds. New plants can begin in several ways. They can grow from cuttings, bulbs, tubers, or spores.

Some new plants grow from cuttings. A **cutting** is a young branch or root cut from an old plant. When a cutting is placed in water or in damp soil, it grows roots. It sprouts stems and leaves. In time, it becomes a new plant just like the old plant it was cut from. Geraniums are often grown from cuttings.

Some new plants grow from bulbs. A **bulb** is a round, underground bud. It is a young plant covered with layers of leaves. The leaves protect the plant and store food for it. Daffodils and tulips grow from bulbs. Onions are bulbs we eat.

Some new plants grow from tubers. A **tuber** is the thick, fat part of an underground stem. The potato is a tuber.

Some new plants grow from spores.

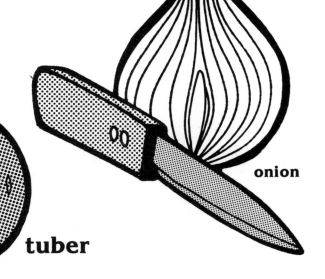

cutting

daffodil

bulbs

onion

tuber

potato

Name _____

What Are Spores?

Some plants do not bloom. Because these plants do not grow flowers, they have no way to make seeds. Instead, they make spores.

Spores are different from seeds in many ways. Spores are smaller than even the smallest seed. Spores do not have a hard shell outside. They do not have a little plant and food for it inside.

But spores are like seeds in one way. They can grow into new plants.

Spores are formed in tiny **sacks** on the leaves and stems of plants. Ferns, mosses, and mushrooms grow from spores.

Find and color the six mushrooms hidden in this picture.

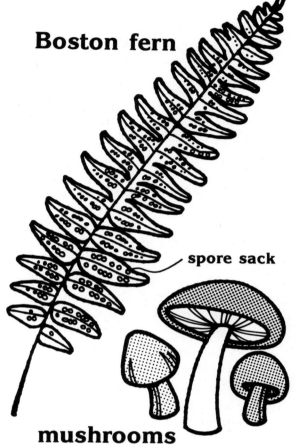

Boston fern

spore sack

mushrooms

Name _____

Plant Fact Hunt

Use this book and other books about plants.
Check each sentence to see if it is **right** or **wrong**.
When you find out, color the correct box.

1. The oldest living things on earth are plants.	right	wrong
2. All plants grow in the ground.	right	wrong
3. Oxygen in the air we breathe comes from green plants.	right	wrong
4. When green plants have light, their leaves can make food from air and water.	right	wrong
5. Nylon and plastic are made from plants.	right	wrong
6. Cereals, cotton, paper, rubber, spices, and some medicines come from plants.	right	wrong
7. A seed is a baby plant.	right	wrong
8. All plants grow from seeds.	right	wrong
9. Plant seeds come from flowers.	right	wrong
10. Bees and other insects help flowers make seeds by carrying pollen from one plant to another.	right	wrong
11. Trees that lose their leaves in the fall are called **evergreen**.	right	wrong
12. A person who studies plants is called a **botanist**.	right	wrong

Name _____

Rhyme Time

When words begin with different sounds but end with the same sound, we say they **rhyme**. The words *book* and *look* rhyme. Some words that end with the same letters do not rhyme. The words *boot* and *foot* do not rhyme. Some words that end with different letters do rhyme. The words *cute* and *root* do rhyme. In each row, circle the one word that rhymes with the first word.

1. corn	cob	seed	thorn
2. flower	daisy	shower	rain
3. fruit	root	apple	food
4. grow	now	green	blow
5. rain	vein	water	run
6. rose	leaf	grows	red
7. seed	food	shell	weed
8. smell	small	swell	nose
9. stalk	walk	stem	trunk
10. tree	wood	bee	plant

Name _____

Plant Poem

Write a poem about a plant on the lines below. Use some of the words listed on page 35 in your poem. Make your poem pretty or funny. Draw a picture to go with your poem on a separate sheet of paper. Cut out your poem. Paste your poem and your picture on a larger sheet of paper.

Example

Why is it that,
When I plant seeds,
And I want flowers,
I get weeds?

_____

_____

_____

_____

_____

_____

_____

Name _____

My Life As a Plant

Pretend that you are a plant. You can be a giant tree that is more than 4,000 years old. You can be a cactus standing in the desert. You can be a vine clinging to the side of a building. You can be kelp floating in the ocean. You can be a tumbleweed rolling across a field. First, decide what kind of plant you are. Then, on the lines below, write a story about something that happens to you.

_____

_____

_____

_____

_____

_____

_____

_____

_____

_____

Name _____

Lots of Leaves

Fascinating Plant Facts

More than 350,000 different kinds of plants grow throughout the world.

Some plants eat insects. The leaves of the Venus's-flytrap attract insects and close around them, trapping them inside. After the plant digests the insects, the leaves open once again.

Most plants grow in the ground, but some grow in other places. Mistletoe grows on the trunks and branches of trees.

Plants that bear cones are called **conifers**. Most conifers have needlelike leaves.

Ferns grow mostly in moist, woody areas. Their leaves are called **fronds**.

The largest living things on earth are giant sequoia trees. They are found only in California.

The drug **cortisone** is made from the roots of a yam. This drug is used to treat people who have arthritis.

Plants are the oldest living things. One bristlecone pine tree is more than 4,000 years old.

Plant Terms and Their Meanings

blade   The broad flat body of any leaf (page 14); also, the long narrow leaf of a grass (page 30).

botanist   A scientist who studies plants (page 34).

bulb   A round, underground bud that is really a young plant covered with layers of leaves (page 32).

cereals   A special group of grasses that produce edible seeds called grains (page 30).

chlorophyll The green material that gives leaves their color and enables them to make food (page 15).

conifers   Plants that bear cones (page 39).

cutting   A young branch or root cut from an old plant. In time, a cutting can grow into a new plant just like the old plant from which it was cut (page 32).

evergreen   The name given to a tree that does *not* lose its leaves in winter (page 34).

flower   The part of a plant that makes seeds so there will be more plants (pages 7 and 17).

fruit   The part of a plant that holds the seeds (page 26).

grain   The small hard edible seeds of cereal grasses (page 30).

grasses   A group of green plants that have jointed stems, long narrow leaves, and spikelike clusters of flowers (page 30).

midrib   The central vein of a leaf, which runs from the base of the leaf blade to its tip (page 14).

needles   The leaves of pine trees and other conifers (pages 11 and 39).

petals   The parts of a flower that are often bright colors and make insects see the flower and come to it (page 18).

Plant Terms and Their Meanings
(continued)

pistil   The center part of a flower that is often sticky and makes seeds (page 18).

plant   Any living thing that is not an animal (page 5).

pollen   A powderlike dust that is often yellow, is held in the stamens, and helps a flower make seeds (page 18).

root   The part of a plant that grows down into the earth, holds the plant in place, and takes water and minerals from the soil to feed the plant (pages 7 and 8).

seed   A special hard-shelled package that holds a baby plant and food for this tiny plant to use until it sprouts leaves and can make its own food (page 22).

sepals   Special leaves that cover and protect the flower bud while it is growing. The sepals open and peel back to let the petals out when the plant blooms (page 18).

spore   A single cell that comes from a plant and, like a seed, can grow into a new plant (page 33).

stalks   The soft bendable stems of plants such as asparagus, broccoli, and celery (page 10).

stamens   The parts of a flower that hold pollen (page 18).

stem   The part of a plant that holds up the leaves and flowers and carries water and minerals from the roots to the leaves (pages 7 and 10); also, the part of a leaf that connects the blade to the plant (page 14).

trunk   The stiff woody stem of a tree (page 10).

tuber   The thick, fat part of an underground stem. The potato is a tuber (page 32).

veins   The parts of a leaf that carry water from the midrib to all parts of the blade (page 14).

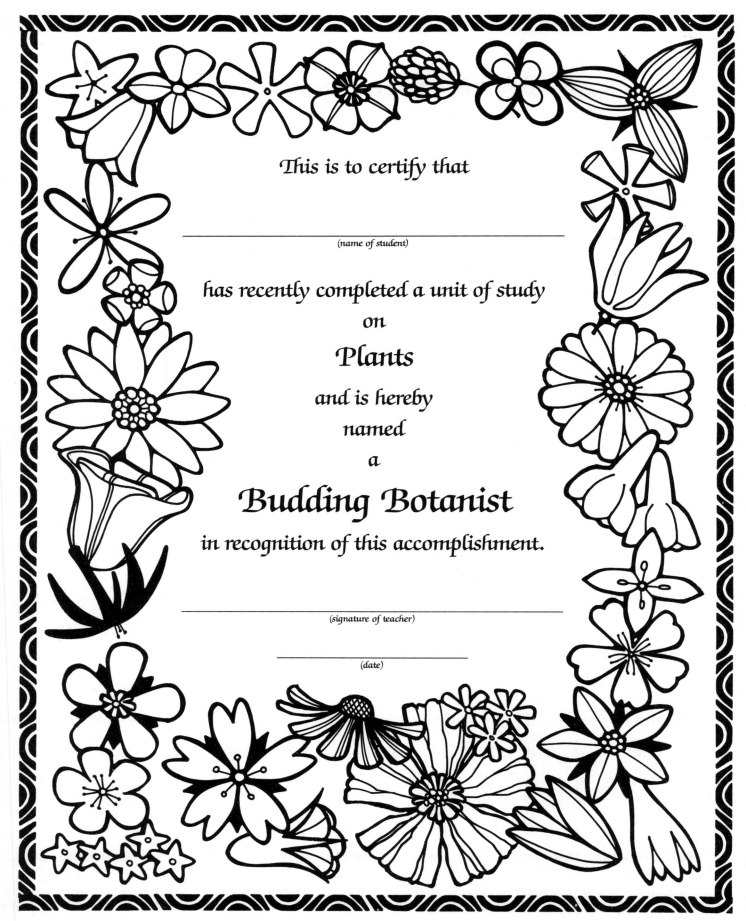

This is to certify that

_____
(name of student)

has recently completed a unit of study

on

Plants

and is hereby

named

a

Budding Botanist

in recognition of this accomplishment.

_____
(signature of teacher)

_____
(date)

Special Plant Awards

Thanks a bunch for _____.

_____

You're a peach of a person!

_____

I have a hunch you could be

the best of the bunch!

Your

_____

has improved!

I'm glad you turned over a new leaf!

_____

Special Plant Awards
(continued)

You're the

apple

of my eye!

_____

You
have
an
"ear"

for

_____ .

Like a seed—
I know

your

_____ skill

will grow!

_____

Your paper
proves
you're a
budding

_____ .

Keep up
the
good work!

_____

Plant Clip Art

Clip art is ideal for decorating announcements, awards, bulletins, fliers, game boards, invitations, name tags, newsletters, notes, posters, or programs.

Most of the illustrations in this book are suitable for use as clip art. To use any drawing in this way, photocopy the page on which it appears (so that the actual book remains intact for later use), cut out the photocopy of the drawing you wish to use, attach this drawing to the sheet you intend to decorate, and photocopy this sheet with the art in place.

Correlated Activities
(for kids to do with adult help)

1. 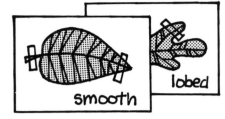 Collect leaves that have **smooth**, **toothed**, **notched**, and **lobed** edges. Tape each leaf to a plain five-inch-by-seven-inch index card. Label each leaf according to the kind of edges it has. If possible, find out what plant each leaf came from. Write the name of the plant on the card also. (**Labeling and Classifying**)

2. Make a seed mosaic by gluing dried beans, corn kernels, peas, and other seeds to a small piece of stiff cardboard. (**Crafts and Creativity**)

3. Seeds are carried from place to place by wind, water, animals, and people. First, learn more about the ways in which seeds travel. Then, draw and color a picture showing one of these ways. (**Locating Information and Communicating Ideas**)

4. Some seeds have hooks. These seeds stick to the fur of animals and to the clothing of people. In late summer or early fall, put on a pair of old white socks *over* your shoes. Walk through an unmowed yard or a field. After your walk, examine the socks to see what seeds stuck to them. With permission, plant one of the socks in the ground. Water your "sock garden" regularly and watch to see what grows. (**Observing and Experiencing**)

5. To a large map of the United States of America, add the picture or name of each state flower. (**Map Awareness and U.S. Geography**)

California Poppy

6. Some plants are harmful. Touching them may make your skin itch or burn. Eating their leaves or fruit may make you sick. Learn more about a plant that is irritating or poisonous. Then create a poster telling classmates how to recognize this plant and warning them to avoid it. (**Understanding Concepts and Communicating Ideas**)

POISON OAK IS NO JOKE!

Answer Key

Page 5, What Is a Plant?
Five plants are pictured on this page: a fruit tree, a tulip, an evergreen tree, a potted plant, and a dandelion.

Page 7, What Are the Parts of a Plant?

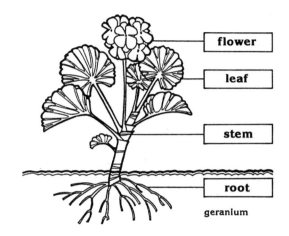

geranium

Page 9, Root Maze

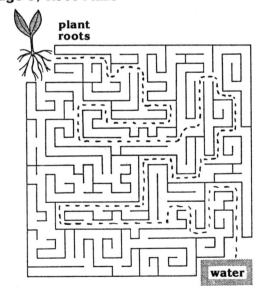

plant roots

water

Page 13, Which Leaf Is Different?
1. c   2. a   3. b   4. d

Page 14, What Are the Parts of a Leaf?

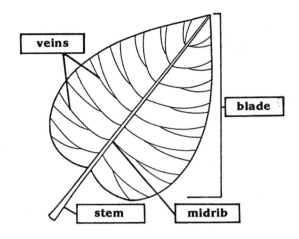

veins   blade   stem   midrib

Page 16, Chlorophyll Crossword

```
            F
   C H L O R O P H Y L L
   A     O   O           E
   B     W   O           A
   B     E   T           F
   A     R   S T A L K
   G         R
S T E M       U
              N E E D L E S
              K
```

Page 19, Flower Power
1. carnation   5. pansy
2. daisy   6. rose
3. iris   7. sunflower
4. lily   8. tulip

Page 20, State Flower Match-Up
1. E   2. A   3. G   4. D
5. F   6. B   7. H   8. C

Page 24, A Seed Becomes a Plant

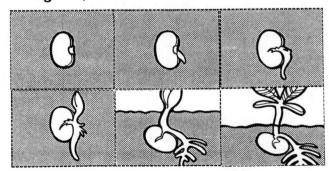

Answer Key
(continued)

Page 25, What Does a Seed Need to Grow?
1. A seed is placed in the ground and watered.
2. The water soaks into the seed.
3. The water makes the plant and food inside the seed swell up.
4. The swollen plant bursts out of the seed.
5. A tiny root pushes down in the soil.
6. A stem with leaves springs out of the ground, reaching for the sunshine.

Page 27, Which Picture Is Different?
1. c   2. b   3. d   4. a

Page 28, A Nutty Puzzle

Page 29, Strawberry Spelling
Answers will vary, but possible words include are, ate, bar, bare, bat, bay, bear, beast, best, ear, eat, east, rare, rat, rest, sat, saw, say, sea, seat, set, sew, star, stay, sweat, tea, tear, tray, try, war, was, water, way, wear, web, west, year, yes, and yet.

Page 33, What Are Spores?

Page 34, Plant Fact Hunt
1. right   5. wrong   9. right
2. wrong   6. right   10. right
3. right   7. right   11. wrong
4. right   8. wrong   12. right

Page 35, Rhyme Time
1. corn–thorn   6. rose–grows
2. flower–shower   7. seed–weed
3. fruit–root   8. smell–swell
4. grow–blow   9. stalk–walk
5. rain–vein   10. tree–bee